THE BIG GREEN POETRY MACHINE

This Green Planet

Edited By Jenni Harrison

First published in Great Britain in 2023 by:

Young Writers
Remus House
Coltsfoot Drive
Peterborough
PE2 9BF
Telephone: 01733 890066
Website: www.youngwriters.co.uk

Printed and bound in the UK by BookPrintingUK
Website: www.bookprintinguk.com
YB0543AZ

FOREWORD

Welcome Reader,

For Young Writers' latest competition The Big Green Poetry Machine, we asked primary school pupils to craft a poem about the world. From nature and environmental issues to exploring their own habitats or those of others around the globe, it provided pupils with the opportunity to share their thoughts and feelings about the world around them.

Here at Young Writers our aim is to encourage creativity in children and to inspire a love of the written word, so it's great to get such an amazing response, with some absolutely fantastic poems. It's important for children to be aware of the world around them and some of the issues we face, but also to celebrate what makes it great! This competition allowed them to express their hopes and fears or simply write about their favourite things. The Big Green Poetry Machine gave them the power of words and the result is a wonderful collection of inspirational and moving poems in a variety of poetic styles.

I'd like to congratulate all the young poets in this anthology; I hope this inspires them to continue with their creative writing.

NATURE   WILDLIFE   INSECTS   EARTH   RECYCLE

CONTENTS

Jack McCaugherty (9)	61
Stevey Park (9)	62

Montgomery Primary Academy, Sparkbrook

Hawwa Maryam (8)	63
Sabirin Jelle (11)	64
Saaliha Khadija (10)	65
Madihah Begum (11)	66
Aminah Haq (10)	67
Waseem Mohammed (11)	68
Muskaan Akhtar (11)	69
Aniyah Zaman (11)	70
Imaan Siddiq (8)	71
Aleeha Akhtar (9)	72
Hannah Bibi (11)	73
Fatimah Zahra Ali (9)	74
Omar Yusuf (8)	75
Aryan Zaman (9)	76
Hafsa Islam (8)	77

Oasis Academy Bank Leaze, Lawrence Weston

Arya Flower (7)	78
Rosie Powell (8)	79
Rosie Mai Watson-True (8)	80
Layla Webb (9)	81
Laci Hicks (9)	82
Ariana Williams (8)	83

Ottershaw Christ Church C of E Junior School, Bousley Rise Ottershaw

Vincent Shi	84
Nila Chandrapalan (8)	86
Seb Simpson (9)	88
Riley Smith (9)	90
Leia Fry (9)	93
Ella Keesing (9)	94
Leo Mans (8)	96
Isabella Fraser-Edwards (8)	97

Chloe Custance (8)	98
Daisy King (8)	100
Gamila Rezk (9)	101
Thomas Glover (9)	102
Iola Wilson (9)	103
Abigail Bailey (9)	104
Mason Binnie (8)	105
Lilly Playford (8)	106
Scarlett Ovenden (9)	107
Oscar Alderman (8)	108
Lilly Tyler (8)	109
Arthur Williams (8)	110
Owen Buckland-Waite (8)	111
Amelie Rippingham (9)	112
Annabelle Spall (8)	113
Jack Dyson (8)	114

Pinewood School, Swindon

Wilf Llewellyn	115
Tabitha Dean (9)	116
Bea Godfree (8)	118
Freya Adderley	119
James Hosken (7)	120
Esme Walmsley (7)	121
Wilfrid Bird (9)	122

Rokeby Primary School, Rugby

Zawe Salahadin (7)	123
Mariyah Ali (7)	124
Rosie Harley (8)	126
Imani-Jane Mwananshiku Mnyanyika (7)	127
Sameeha Ali (8)	128
Nela Saja (8)	129
Veronica Barnes (8)	130
Millie Roche (7)	131
Olly Stanhope (7)	132
Izaiah Franklin (6)	133
Iumê Santiago (7)	134
Kara Barnes (5)	135
Daisy King (6)	136
Ethan Bingham (5)	137

Meddina Marissa (8)	138
Chevelle-Coco Marsden-Knole (6)	139
Elliott King (5)	140
Roxy Whisker (7)	141
Luna Watts (7)	142
Matilda Rose Gravell (5)	143
Matthew Barnes (8)	144
Lauren Ashby (6)	145
Charlie Major (7)	146
Harry Lusty Rule (5)	147
Bailey Purchon (5)	148
Brodie Spence (5)	149
Harvey White (6)	150
Edy Soare (8)	151
Karolina Biczak (5)	152

Sandfield Close Primary School, Leicester

Nyah Pau (6)	153
Abheer Shetty (10)	154
Kush Damani	155

Saviour CE Primary School, Collyhurst

Lacey-Mae Gandy (8)	156
Ayomide Oyebade (8)	157
Ivy	158
Lillie	159
Teliah Kayembe (7)	160
Josephine Awotide (8)	161
Abel Peter Jinu	162
Brogan Bobmanuel (7)	163
Azeemat	164
Daisy Burgess (8)	165
Eleri Vincent (7)	166
Jaron	167
Tasia	168
Jack Wilds (8)	169
Lyla	170
Tiara	171
Owen	172

Dia	173
Jacob	174
Mustafa	175
Ralphy	176

St Leonards School, St Andrews

Maryam Al-Saowaf (9)	177
Michelle Chernin (9)	178
Jos Norris-Mbedzi (10)	180
George Cheape (9)	182
Dylan Pyne-Carter (9)	183
Martha Kavanagh (9)	184
Elin Tausch (9)	185
Claudia Breen (9)	186
Isabella Hawkins (9)	187
Thea Steven (10)	188
Abdulla Al Ajami (9)	189
Priya Myles (9)	190
Amber McGhee (9)	191

St Martin's Preparatory School, Grimsby

Ibrahim Mukhtar (8)	192
Zayn Zafar (9)	194
Noel Gacs (8)	195
Aideen Brusby (8)	196
Tatenda Mutondo (8)	198
Henry Evans (8)	199
Felix Bristow (9)	200

Townhill Community School, Townhill

Amelia Philips (6)	201
Rossi-Leigh Davies (7)	202
Shae Griffin (7)	203
Olivia Williams (7)	204
Kieran Lott (7)	205
Isla-Rae Pryor (7)	206
Stefan Hascec (6)	207
Kiki Morris (7)	208
Elodi-Mai Norman (7)	209

Varna Community Primary School, Openshaw

THE POEMS

Climate Change

C ars go around polluting the air, harmful gases fill the air,

L eave the car at home to help our globe last forever,

I magine the difference that we could make together,

M ore and more pollution enters our Earth's atmosphere every day,

A s I blink the Earth is falling and our home is dying,

T he forests don't go on forever you know,

E veryone needs to help before it's too late.

C ountries are getting way too hot,

H elp our Earth, it needs your help to survive,

A re you being innocent or are you throwing rubbish into my seas?

N ever give up your hard work trying to save the planet,

G lobal warming is a big problem so let's try to save the ice caps,

E veryone, look what you have done to our Earth.

Ollie Smith (9)

All Souls' Catholic Primary School, Chapelfields

Help!

What have you done?
You've made me as hot as the sun!
Scientists warned you,
But you carried on like you always do.

It started with the Industrial Revolution,
Which caused tons of harmful pollution.
Then came the invading plastic,
The effects of which were simply drastic.

This caused the globe to start warming,
Where I really sent you a warning!
My skin is getting sunburnt,
But yet you still haven't learned.

As my innocent animals are dying,
You and your people keep on flying.
You're annihilating my precious habitats,
Destroying the homes of wildcats.

Plastic is filling my seas,
So I implore you to stop this, please!

You need to act now and work together,
To keep me like this forever and ever.

Surely you know you can reuse,
And make an effort to eat local produce.
I could be saying my last words now,
So you need to change and you know how.

Nicholas Smith Ortiz (9)

All Souls' Catholic Primary School, Chapelfields

Climate Change: Save The World

C hange the world because our climate temperature is rising.

L ess birds are flying and I am crying.

I f you ignore me, soon it will be your mourning.

M y time here is dying and yours is flying.

A mbitions for you will then turn you into a fool.

T ouching me with pain will never make me your gain.

E at less dairy and meat, it will help your diet and please animals.

C utting back on flying would make the atmosphere recover.

H aving no pollution will make an Earthtacular difference.

A ttack the plastic from the sea, even the trees might bleed.

N ow there's global warming, scientists gave you this warning.

G reen spaces are key, I thought you would've agreed.

E verything around me is a diabolical problem, all because of you and your greed.

Reginald Kirrane (9)

All Souls' Catholic Primary School, Chapelfields

Forgive And Forget

I have a warning,
About global warming,
You might want to hear this,
Turning off the lights you can never miss.

What is all the fuss?
Just start taking the bus,
Because of your behaviour,
Wildlife is in danger.

Recycle your toys,
Girls and boys,
Plastic is invading the sea,
While you are just there sipping your tea.

Stop cutting down my trees,
You need them to breathe,
Respect our green space,
And definitely don't waste.

Leave the car at home when you can,
Choose to walk instead of driving a van,

Animals are dying,
While you are still flying.

Natural disasters,
They are occurring faster and faster,
They are becoming more common,
The damage we are doing won't be forgotten.

Aoife O'Connor (10)
All Souls' Catholic Primary School, Chapelfields

Climate Change

C ome quick! Our world is becoming polluted,

L ight is useful but do you really need it all day? Just use the sun anyway,

I 'm dying, you don't understand, you know there's no Planet B,

M ight you know there's lovely nature out there, but it might go,

A nimals are dying because you're not doing anything about it,

T rees, trees, come, I need to breathe,

E co-friendly, yes, be more eco-friendly or I may die.

C oncrete jungle destroying your woodlands,

H elp, our world is dying because you're not trying,

A ll of us need to work together,

N ow it's the time to make change,

G o out and be the next Greta Thunberg,

E arth is calling so listen to what it's saying.

Rosie Wilkins (9)

All Souls' Catholic Primary School, Chapelfields

You Are The Cause!

Come, help me! I'm crying and dying,
Because of your behaviour wildlife is in danger,
You burn up fossil fuels into the sky,
You throw plastic into my pools of tears,
But as life goes on I get warmer and warmer,
But you don't care, you just pierce me with fear,
This nightmare began with the Industrial
Revolution,
Which caused it to pump out way too much
pollution,
You cut down my trees which made animals leave,
You then started flying and I admit I felt like crying,
But then you didn't stop there, you continued to
wreck the Earth without a single care,
As I blink my seasons change,
I wish things weren't so out of range,
So if we come together we can slow down all this
weather,
Everybody should come together.

Percy Bedjabeng (10)
All Souls' Catholic Primary School, Chapelfields

My Eco Poem

Look at me,
I'm being destroyed,
You need to act fast,
Otherwise, I will be void.

You need to do your part,
To help me, planet Earth,
Otherwise, I will fall apart,
And what will I be worth?

I sigh and cry,
While you watch me die,
So you should,
Reduce, reuse and recycle.

It all started during the Industrial Revolution,
Where there was dirty pollution,
Then came the plastic,
Which was not fantastic.

You can stop this,
By doing your part,

You just need to,
Make this start.

You destroy me,
What have you done?
It's your last chance,
Because I'm at breaking point.

Save me,
Or I will die,
It's getting warmer,
I am not a hot sauna.

Joseph Clancy (9)
All Souls' Catholic Primary School, Chapelfields

Save The Earth

C an you help us preserve our home?

L oudly howling, Earth screams for help,

I f we all make one change, Earth will be a better place,

M ake a difference, no matter how small,

A ll of this began in the Industrial Revolution, which changed our planet's evolution,

T ectonic plates moaning, yelling for help,

E at less meat and dairy.

C ome on people! End using single-use items,

H ere there is no Planet B to rely on,

A cascade of plastic engulfing our oceans,

N ature is dying whilst we carry on flying,

G lobal warming is getting rid of Greenland,

E at more local produce! So now you know how to change the Earth, help us to.

Zachary Alfie Carter Collister (9)

All Souls' Catholic Primary School, Chapelfields

Climate Change

C ome, I am in your home, now melting skin and bone,

L ove me because my joint is at breaking point,

I am dying and you have sent me crying,

M end me, don't bend me,

A im for the goal to help my poor soul,

T ry to help instead of making me yelp,

E scape the evil my people are creating.

C hange your ways for better days,

"H elp me," I plead,

A ttempt to not change me,

N ow help before I die, because I'm not ready to say goodbye,

G et up because there's no Planet B and you're not allowed to flee,

E arth is my name and I can't handle this pain.

Christian Lacey (10)

All Souls' Catholic Primary School, Chapelfields

Eco-Awareness Poem

C an you help tackle climate change?
L ook at what you've done!
I nside this world is too much pollution.
M aking car fumes is bad for the Earth.
A ll around us, God's world is dying.
T hink about changes you can make!
E veryone needs to make a difference!

C utting back on pollution and flying will make a change.
H elp the atmosphere and reduce our carbon footprint.
A ll of your pollution is useless to Gaia!
N one of this is good for our amazing planet.
G lobal warming needs to be intercepted.
E nd this now.

Joshua Tarpey (9)
All Souls' Catholic Primary School, Chapelfields

Climate Change

C limate change is a disaster,

L eave the Earth, she is our master,

I magine the difference we could make together,

M any bodies as one forever,

A s I blink more trees are gone,

T he forests do not go on and on,

E very day I dream of animals.

C uriously, exploring the world's botanicals,

H ave you thought about our polluted air?

A s the Earth says that this is not fair,

N ot tomorrow but right now,

G o and save our planet, but how?

E veryone has to work together to give our world
a happily ever after!

Evie Greenwood (9)

All Souls' Catholic Primary School, Chapelfields

Climate Change

C arbon dioxide is killing Earth.
L iving creatures are dying so stop flying.
I am telling you, there's no Planet B.
M elting ice caps are endangering animals
A s you lie back thinking everything is good.
T he seas are turning black, trees might crack
E arth is melting, let's pull this back.

C an't you try to fix Earth?
H elp us rebuild our beautiful planet
A fter all, it's our turf.
N egative changes are coming our way
G ather together to stop this force.
E veryone can do their part.

Leo Hastings (9)

All Souls' Catholic Primary School, Chapelfields

Our Planet: Earth

C ut consumption and waste,
L et's make this world better,
I ncreasing global temperatures,
M aking harmful gases fill the air,
A ffecting our world,
T rees are dying, the seas are crying,
E at less meat and dairy, plant more trees.

C ut back on flying to create cleaner air,
H elp the Earth to grow and get better by not
littering,
A nimals are dying so please help them all!
N o more thinking of just yourself,
G aia needs saving and needs your help,
E verybody working together is a powerful tool.

Lyla Rose Parkin (9)
All Souls' Catholic Primary School, Chapelfields

Climate Change

C ut back now because the climate is cursed
L ove our planet, do not make it worse
I f we make big changes
M aybe one day we will see
A void waste and consumption because there is no Planet B!
T his is our world, so you need to think twice
E arth is dying so please treat it nicely!

C reate your own green space
H elping the world to heal
A ll can make a difference
N ot attacking our human race
G ather all your knowledge, reduce our carbon footprint
E ach day is not a slow race, this is now a sprint.

Riley Biggs (9)

All Souls' Catholic Primary School, Chapelfields

Climate Change

C an you help my caring, loving planet?
L et's plant lush, green trees to help us breathe.
I ce is melting in Antarctica.
M ake a difference however small, *you can!*
A nimals are dying, we're still flying.
T ry to avoid single-use items.
E arth is getting sunburnt because of you.

C ut consumption and waste.
H ere there is no Planet B.
A re you throwing your litter into my seas?
N atural to you is harmful to me.
G reen spaces respect and protect.
E at less meat and dairy.

Grace Hawkins (9)
All Souls' Catholic Primary School, Chapelfields

My Eco Poem

C an you listen to me, for a minute?
L ook at our lovely planet,
I t is being destroyed,
M any do not realise, it is happening, rapidly,
A ct quickly or our beloved planet will be no more!
T he ice caps are melting while we sit and do nothing,
E veryone needs to make a difference!

C ars are putting bad fumes in the air,
H elp tackle climate change,
A lot of trees are being destroyed,
N ever do this again, please,
G ases are also contributing to this,
E nd this now!

Jonah Gallagher (10)

All Souls' Catholic Primary School, Chapelfields

Our Planet

C limate change is happening fast
L ast chance to save our world
I 'll do something if you do too
M other Earth is falling apart
A part from the world coming away
T hink of animals crying to sleep
E very living thing losing homes.

C ome help because soon it will all be gone
H appy are you, but look at the world
A sk yourself, "What can I do?"
N o more plastic means no more pain
G et ready because soon it will go away
E very word in this poem is true.

Terrelle Etta Dusty Baker (9)
All Souls' Catholic Primary School, Chapelfields

Work Together Today!

C limate change is happening,
L and is falling down,
I am your only hope,
M ake the Earth cooler,
A nimals are dying,
T he world is on fire,
E veryone can make a difference.

C ome help me quickly,
H ave hope in me,
A ll around us is trash,
N o Planet B,
G ive me more green spaces,
E at less meat and dairy.

Let's work together as one for our planet today,
To keep our Earth spinning, do not delay!

Isabel Michael Etura (10)

All Souls' Catholic Primary School, Chapelfields

Climate Change

C limates are changing
L ands are flooding
I ce is melting
M ore and more harm
A ction needs to happen
T oday, not tomorrow
E ndangered animals need your help.

C ruelly destroyed
H elp by making good things happen
A ny of you can
N ow we are aware
G o and make the changes
E veryone needs to help save our planet.

Darren Twum Boateng (9)

All Souls' Catholic Primary School, Chapelfields

Water Whale

As litter goes through me I cry.
As people kill my friends I sigh.
You destroy my home
And you wouldn't like it if I did that to you.
I know I'm a whale, not as smart,
But trust me, you're destroying my heart.
Please save my friends by recycling,
Not throwing it into the sea.
I know there are good people out there
So trust me, please, you won't change your mind.

Bea O'Neill (9)
Holy Rosary Catholic Primary School, Aintree

Stop The Pollution Crisis

Pollution is killing me,
Can't you see?
The plastic you waste
All ends up in the sea,
You have cut my trees,
You have littered my ground,
I am looking around
And no home can be found.

Yet there is a way to stop this crisis,
And a way to treat me a bit nicer,
Help me and spread the word,
Stop littering,
If you do this,
The planet will be mightier.

Zaira Di Francescantonio (10)
Holy Rosary Catholic Primary School, Aintree

Turtles Are Dying

T o save the turtles we must stop littering and start binning

U nder the sea there is so much rubbish that turtles are dying

R educe, reuse, recycle to save the turtles

T urtles are worth saving

L ove our Earth and stop littering!

E arth is worth saving too!

S aving the turtles is like saving ourselves!

Emily Hornblower (9)

Holy Rosary Catholic Primary School, Aintree

Nature Needs Help

Grass is green, grass is green
Oh, how lovely it is.
We need to stop climate change
If we want it to change.
Cut down my trees, no grass is found
Look all around, nothing is found.
The world needs you
And I need you to *help* our world
Don't look at me in hate
As I look at you in anger.

Gabrielle Beckwith (9)
Holy Rosary Catholic Primary School, Aintree

Summer's Come

Summer has come across the sun,
Flowers dancing and prancing.
You should be excited for it to spring
By having a lovely sing.
The environment needs you to help litterbugs
And after you can have fun hugs with all your
friends.
You should be aware of a scare
When litter comes and hurts the flowers and
nature.

Pippa Wright (9)

Holy Rosary Catholic Primary School, Aintree

Litter Is Not For Life

Litter is not for life,
Think of the fish in the sea,
Endangered by the creation made for peace.
So don't throw when you go to the beach,
Pick it up, let the turtles be free!

Annie Irvine (11)

Holy Rosary Catholic Primary School, Aintree

How Animals Are Going Extinct

My home is destroyed!
You cut down my trees
Pollute my air
Fill my land with rubbish
I can't find a home to live in!

Maisie Metcalf (9)

Holy Rosary Catholic Primary School, Aintree

Katie Lou Learns To Recycle

Katie Lou was a great big poo
Because she never recycled
She was so bad but she got very mad
And threw a great big tantrum
But one boring night a fairy took flight
To try and find a solution
She flew into the house as quiet as a mouse
"Argh! What are you?" Katie screamed
"Do not fear, Katie dear, I've come to find a solution"
"Okay, I will try it, but I still do not buy it"
In a flash she was at the river
And all she could see was litter
Poor little animals, this must be tough
I've really had enough
So from that day she changed her ways
And now she knows how to recycle.

Tia Porter (11)
Icollege Inspiration, Thatcham

Recycle

R euse bottles, the

E nvironment is precious,

C lean planet,

Y ou can't throw plastic in the ocean,

C ompost your fruit,

L ook after trees,

E veryone, don't chop down trees.

Ciara Horton (8)

Icollege Inspiration, Thatcham

Our Planet

G et ready to

R ecycle and change the

E arth and help save the

E nvironment.

N ature is a big part of our planet and we have to help save it.

Joshua Riley (10)

Icollege Inspiration, Thatcham

Recycle

R euse

E lectricity

C ardboard boxes

Y oghurt pots

C ling film

L eaves

E cofriendly.

Blake Bowyer (9)

Icollege Inspiration, Thatcham

Huffling Hedgehog

There's a snuffling hedgehog in the scattering
leaves,
Waiting for hibernation.
Soft and sweet but fierce and ferocious,
It scurries through the bushes,
Whining, moaning throughout the day.
A four-legged mammal,
I doubt it's that bad.
It's only wee, calm down.
Aye, but it's a wee menace,
So watch what you're doing.
It may be wee, warm and cute,
But it's got pine needles on there.
Some folks hate and some folks don't,
I don't blame them to say,
"Beware of the huffling hedgehog!"

Faith Gibson (11)
Lochnorris Primary School, Cumnock

The Seasons

Life starts with spring
Warm sunshine feels awesome
Buds grow, leaves they bring
Trees are beautiful with blossom
Summer sun scorches the Earth
Dark brown branches full of leaves
Giving shade for all it's worth
Making oxygen, it achieves
Autumn leaves are so pretty
The red and orange colours are so bold
Stepping on leaves that are crispy
The air is getting cold
The bitter wind is blowing
Grass all white with frost
The heavy grey sky is snowing
The trees in winter look lost.

Molly Sloan (11)
Lochnorris Primary School, Cumnock

What Am I?

What am I?
I blend with my surroundings,
I'm in the Animalia kingdom,
And I live in Africa,
What am I?

What am I?
I'm in the Animalia kingdom,
I have bright yellow eyes,
I live in the rainforest,
What am I?

What am I?
I'm in the Animalia kingdom,
I live in Lake Xochimilco in Mexico,
And I have six gills,
What am I?

Answers: A chameleon, an ocelot and an axolotl.

Ryan Mason (11)
Lochnorris Primary School, Cumnock

YoungWriters® Est. 1991

Rainforest

R ich in plant life
A bundance of animals
I nteresting insects
N ew species being discovered
F orest, I love how I walk through you
O verflowing waterfalls around me
R ain falling down onto my head
E arthy smells linger in my nose
S unlight poking through the trees
T weeting birds sing to me on my walk.

Bonnie Taylor
Lochnorris Primary School, Cumnock

What Am I?

I am as fast as a fox
And as blue as the bright sky,
Yet as still as a deer in headlights,
Everything needs me, including you,
However, if I wanted to, I could kill you,
You can see right through me,
I am strong but I can't fight you,
What am I?

Answer: Water.

Khloe Mahood (11)
Lochnorris Primary School, Cumnock

Winter's Morning

W inter's morning, not a cloud in the sky.

I n the house, nobody shall cry.

N ot a sound outside, only the birds chirping.

T he sky as blue as a dolphin.

E verybody nice and happy.

R obin red breast beats the winter cold by singing a beautiful song.

Harris Baird (11)

Lochnorris Primary School, Cumnock

What Am I?

I carry my own house,
I'm a vegetarian,
I leave a trail everywhere I go,
In my eyes I am fast
But in your eyes I'm slow,
I change my house very often,
You find me in grass or in the open,
What am I?

Answer: A snail.

Arron Henderson (11)
Lochnorris Primary School, Cumnock

Nature

What I can see is a lot of greenness
The greenness is grass and trees and a plant
And I can also see red roses
And also I can see a beautiful waterfall
I can see the sun shining bright into my eyes
So brightly it could pop out my eye.

Kalvin Harris (9)

Lochnorris Primary School, Cumnock

Nature

M oon shining brightly
O n us below
O ver all the Earth
N ight light in the sky.

M oon shining brightly
O n us below
O h how beautiful
N ight light in the sky.

Kieran Dick (9)

Lochnorris Primary School, Cumnock

Sleeping Sloths

I live in the rainforest,
I am very slow
And I am normally spotted in a zoo.
I climb trees
And I love eating leaves.
I watch out for predators from the trees
And I sleep a lot.
I am very playful.

Alfie Marshall (10)
Lochnorris Primary School, Cumnock

The Beautiful Blue Ocean

Over the rocks, along the sand,
A beautiful blue ocean lies in its path.
The powerful waves
And the bright sun giving you sunburn.
And when it's sunset,
It's the most beautiful thing in the world.

Ross Brown (11)
Lochnorris Primary School, Cumnock

Rain

Rain
Pitter patter
The gentle sound of raindrops
As they tumble down the window
Rain
Bringing life, giving water
To animals, plants and fauna
Rain
Pitter patter
Pitter patter.

Evie Knox (11)
Lochnorris Primary School, Cumnock

The Forest Fairies

The people of nature were mystical creatures of the forest.
One day, my friends and I were walking.
It was the forest fairies, it was a beautiful night,
The moon was bright, it was beautiful like midnight.

Orla Baillie (9)
Lochnorris Primary School, Cumnock

Earth

E arth spinning around the sun
A ll year seasons one on one
'R ound the garden plants grow
T all and strong, row upon row
H arvest time will soon be here.

Jaxon Lyle (9)
Lochnorris Primary School, Cumnock

Day And Birds

B right and shining sun.
I n the tree there are birds.
R attling, tweeting, singing.
D oes a lot of plastic get in?
S un is going down, now it is night.

Zara-Jane Sykes (11)
Lochnorris Primary School, Cumnock

Saturn

S tay in one place
A s rocks go past me
T ime flies past every day
U p so far in the universe
R ainbow galaxies above me
N ever let me go.

Cooper Bryce (9)
Lochnorris Primary School, Cumnock

The Little Koala

K ing of the eucalyptus tree,
O n a big bough dozing,
A dorable,
L oving but lazy,
A ustralian,
S uper at climbing.

Kayleigh McEwan (9)
Lochnorris Primary School, Cumnock

River

R ushing water

I nteresting pathway

V ariety of wildlife and plant life it holds

E bbs and flows

R ipples from fish jumping.

Kody Paton (10)

Lochnorris Primary School, Cumnock

Daisy

A daisy is a flower.
The daisy comes out in late spring
And also the colours of a daisy are white and
yellow.
You can find the daisy in fields and grass areas.

Ellie Cowan (10)
Lochnorris Primary School, Cumnock

Nature Is Beautiful

Nature has lots of different colours and smells.
Every walk you take has a story to tell.
I like sitting next to the river to see how fast it will flow.

Abbie Smillie (11)
Lochnorris Primary School, Cumnock

Fish

Fish big and small
You catch them for dinner
They live in a river big
And small oceans and seas
Pacific and Atlantic
Sunfish, clownfish.

Nathan Crawford (11)
Lochnorris Primary School, Cumnock

What Am I?

I grow on trees
I'm soft when young
But hard when old
Squirrels and birds love me
What am I?

Answer: A pine cone.

Finlay Weir (10)
Lochnorris Primary School, Cumnock

Outside

Being outside it is amazing
Seeing the animals is very great
Up in a tree
Or under the soil
And up in the sky
We are killing it all.

George Byrne (11)
Lochnorris Primary School, Cumnock

Who Am I?

I am round
I am massive
I am orange and yellow
I am up high
I shine down on Earth
Who am I?

Answer: The sun.

William Bryce (9)

Lochnorris Primary School, Cumnock

The Beach

On the sunny beach of the Bahamas,
The ghost-white sand on the beach
And the bright, crystal-blue water
Hitting the jagged, black rocks.

Riley McGoogan (10)
Lochnorris Primary School, Cumnock

What Am I?

I am old,
I grow outside,
I am purple,
Just be careful not to touch me,
I can be spiky.

Answer: A thistle.

Kayla Scott (9)
Lochnorris Primary School, Cumnock

Space

S un, stars
P lanets
A stronauts exploring
C omets zooming
E xtraterrestrials, are they real?

Jack McCaugherty (9)
Lochnorris Primary School, Cumnock

Spring

I was on a high tree.
The moon was so light.
The sun was very yellow.
The flowers were so, so pretty.

Stevey Park (9)
Lochnorris Primary School, Cumnock

Recycling

Our government encourages us to recycle
Not everything, but just the bits they choose
Empty tin cans, bottles, glass and plastic
Paper and the list goes on
However, on the downside, and one I cannot
fathom
We recycle plastic bottles but not their plastic caps
No reason given
We recycle paper but not the paper envelopes
The glue glumps up the works!
Charities collect plastic bottle tops and recycle
them there
But not us, no, we cannot put them in
Plastic shopping bags for life are not recycled by
us
But some supermarkets can!

Hawwa Maryam (8)
Montgomery Primary Academy, Sparkbrook

Around The World

Sitting underneath a tree
Looking out as far as you can see
Rubbish mixed with brown dead leaves
Around, below, above, near me
Do people choose what not to see
The animals must suffer and die
Work as a team, recycle and change
The way we live, grow crops, the bees
Mixed with our care of breathing trees
Earth has done so much for me
For you, for animals on land and sea
Communities must reunite and plan a path
towards light
With speed, goodwill and all our might.

Sabirin Jelle (11)
Montgomery Primary Academy, Sparkbrook

Northern Lights

Night is dark
Out of reach, vast and stark
Rays of candyfloss, emerald green
Thrilling colours all so clear
Halo of glory
Enveloping beauty
Ripples of light
Nature's best
Looking in wonder this natural jewel
It's hard to believe that it's real
Galaxy contender
Highlights of the sky
Teasing, playing hide-and-seek
Showing magic when it pleases.

Saaliha Khadija (10)
Montgomery Primary Academy, Sparkbrook

Nature

The baby blue sky was sleepy and still
A round golden medal blinking up high
Colourful dancers reach for the sky
Growing, growing as tall as can be
Beautiful, vibrant buds ready to burst
Gentle drops of rain quenching their thirst
Mother nature, a friend or a foe
A creator of beauty in life and of death
From seed until taking our very last breath.

Madihah Begum (11)
Montgomery Primary Academy, Sparkbrook

Autumn Leaves

Autumn leaves, oh autumn's here
Falling, falling every year
Oh winter is so, so near
Waiting for mornings crispy clear
Red, orange, brown, drifting all around
Trick or treat, lots to eat
Smell of burning everywhere
Bang! Bang! Vibrant colours fill the air
Autumn's leaves, oh autumn's here
My favourite time of year.

Aminah Haq (10)
Montgomery Primary Academy, Sparkbrook

Pollution

P lastic is making me cry

O h why, oh why, oh why?

L ooking for food but nothing to find

L uscious living left far behind

U gly plastic choking animals

T hink of how we cause them pain

I t's time to end this and ban all plastic!

O h why, oh why, oh why?

N o more delay as this is drastic!

Waseem Mohammed (11)

Montgomery Primary Academy, Sparkbrook

Penguins

P enguins walking just like humans
E arth is warming up, not good, not good!
N o one is trying hard enough
G etting food can be so tough
U nderwater swimming to live, flip-flap!
I n their shrinking ice home still alive
N ot so easy now to survive
S ave this precious species with an SOS for penguins!

Muskaan Akhtar (11)

Montgomery Primary Academy, Sparkbrook

Pollution

P rotect our planet from revolting rubbish
O pportunities to make the world a better place
L eave a clean world
L egacy free from all problems
U nite as one to clean our planet Earth
T ake action now!
I ntentions become actions
O pen the door to your mind
N ow, now, now don't stop!

Aniyah Zaman (11)

Montgomery Primary Academy, Sparkbrook

Saving Our Environment

E nvironment
N eeds help now!
V ery essential
I mportant
'R ound the world animals are hurting
O ur oceans are polluted
N ets trap more than fish
M aking animals die
E veryone needs to help now!
N ot later, the time to help is now!
T ime is running out.

Imaan Siddiq (8)

Montgomery Primary Academy, Sparkbrook

What Am I?

I am surrounded by trees
Most of my parts are green
I am good for animal habitats
Some of me have streams or lakes
Every December can light the way
I keep you supplied with food and paper
What am I?

Answer: A forest.

Aleeha Akhtar (9)
Montgomery Primary Academy, Sparkbrook

Koalas

K oalas often climb up high
O n the lookout for bamboo
A ustralia, their beloved home
L ots of sleep without a peep
A verage life is rather brief
S oftly snoring in the breeze.

Hannah Bibi (11)

Montgomery Primary Academy, Sparkbrook

Pollution

A kennings poem

Fish killer
Recycle nightmare
Animal starver
Rat breeder
Ocean vandal
Wild animal foe
Disease bringer
Clean water destroyer
Fly-tipper
Nature's enemy.

Fatimah Zahra Ali (9)
Montgomery Primary Academy, Sparkbrook

Recycle

R ubbish, rubbish

E verywhere

C lutter, clutter

Y ou should care

C are for land, care for sea

L iving creatures

E verywhere.

Omar Yusuf (8)

Montgomery Primary Academy, Sparkbrook

Earth

E nvironmentally friendly
A lways protect our planet
R easons for climate change
T hings that destroy our world
H elp us save our Earth.

Aryan Zaman (9)

Montgomery Primary Academy, Sparkbrook

Earth

E arth, our Earth
A ll around us day by day
R espect it with
T olerance, care, then shower it with
H appiness and spread it everywhere.

Hafsa Islam (8)

Montgomery Primary Academy, Sparkbrook

Animals All Around

Birds in the tree,
Shout, "Let me free!"
Rabbits underground,
Shout, "Don't hunt our land!"

Turtles in the sea,
Shout, "Come help me!"
Sheep in the field,
Shout, "Don't use our land!"

Squirrels in the tree,
Shout, "Don't you see?"
Hedgehogs in the leaves,
Shout, "Don't uncover our home!"

Arya Flower (7)
Oasis Academy Bank Leaze, Lawrence Weston

Save The Poor Planet!

If you are done with a plastic box
Don't put it outside because you will harm the
foxes
Did you know that if you hurt the Earth
Nothing is left of worth?

Did you know if you drop litter
It will stay there and glitter?
Did you know that to find litter
You can use a litter picker?

Rosie Powell (8)

Oasis Academy Bank Leaze, Lawrence Weston

How To Look After The Planet

Did you know if you drop a plastic spoon,
It will cause us doom?
Marine litter is about fish in the sea,
It can squish them in one, two, three.

If fish get stuck,
They stop breathing so they need luck.
You need to have a paper bag,
And you need a green flag.

Rosie Mai Watson-True (8)
Oasis Academy Bank Leaze, Lawrence Weston

Save The Unhealthy Planet

Haiku poetry

Litter is dropping.
Plastic is bad for the world.
Stop littering now!

Plastic can harm us.
Litter is bad for people.
It is pollution.

We can pick it up.
The plastic that is around.
Follow the three Rs!

Layla Webb (9)

Oasis Academy Bank Leaze, Lawrence Weston

Stopping Marine Litter

Haiku poetry

Stop littering now!
We need to save the planet,
It is important.

We can recycle,
Littering is bad for all,
We can stop this now.

It will get lethal,
We should put it in the bin,
We need to save fish.

Laci Hicks (9)

Oasis Academy Bank Leaze, Lawrence Weston

Save The Energy

Turn off the light,
When it is night,
Solar panels in the air,
To show that we care,
Off the light goes,
Like nobody knows,
How much energy we save,
Hip hip hooray!

Ariana Williams (8)

Oasis Academy Bank Leaze, Lawrence Weston

The Rainforest

Animals are endangered
What do you think you can do?
Trees are getting chopped down
And animals losing their homes
They'll soon become hungry
Since we take away their food
What do you think you can do to save the animals?

Humans taking away their land
Using it for houses and factories
Can you help stop them before it's too late?
A crane here, an excavator there
The rainforest will soon be gone
Poaching animals, killing them
How would you like that?

Help now! Help now!
Animals are endangered!
Some people are cutting down trees
The animals have now lost their protection
Can't you help?
Don't just stand there, don't just sit there

Hurry up and help!
They have lost their homes
And more than sixty percent of the rainforests are gone
What do you think you can do to save the animals?

Help! Help!
What do you think you can do?
Hurry! Hurry!
Can you save the animals?
Please help! Please help!
Animals are endangered!
What do you think you can do to save the animals?

Hurry up and save the animals!
Animals are isolated
Animals are lost
Animals are getting killed
Animals are dying
Save them!
What do you think you can do to save the animals?

Vincent Shi

Ottershaw Christ Church C of E Junior School, Bousley Rise Ottershaw

Help The Planet Survive

We have all seen animals before,
Living happily in their homes.
But now they say:
"Why destroy our one place to live?
We're poor and innocent."
Hurry, hurry,
It's dreadful.
Hurry, hurry,
You're destroying the Earth.
So are you just going to sit and watch
The precious, loving creatures lose their homes
Or are you going to help?
How would you like it if your home was destroyed?
Trees are dying,
Giving us less oxygen,
Also giving the poor, defenceless animals nowhere
to go,
Leaving them to shiver out in the cold.
Are you going to help save them?
Most of us are guilty of what we're doing
But some of us are not,

So if you are feeling that way,
You will know what you need to do!
Plant trees and anything green,
You make them die
But you don't realise that they keep you alive
And provide medicine along with our daily needs.
Hurry, hurry,
Don't kill Earth.
Hurry, hurry,
Help Earth survive.
So how are you going to help keep Earth alive?

Nila Chandrapalan (8)

Ottershaw Christ Church C of E Junior School, Bousley Rise
Ottershaw

The Start Of The End

So we all know the rainforest
You know, where tigers,
Snakes, monkeys and spiders
All live, well, people are going
In and taking them to the zoo
So instead of sitting on the toilet taking a poo
Help the animals get out of there, dude.

Sure, it might be dangerous
But the parents might be curious
So instead of sitting on the couch
Help the animals get out and about.

Some animals are almost to extinction
So before you go hunting take a prediction
Of the human race
Instead of putting an animal in a cage.

So if you see an animal in need
Help it with maybe a weed
To help it cure its broken bone
Instead of going somewhere on your phone.

Just hear their yelp for help
So stop going to a shop and trying on a belt.

Oh, I guess you need more info
Well first don't name your chameleon Gizmo
Instead, just let it free
So it can see its family.

Well that's the end now
Hope you enjoyed
And stop treating animals like
A muddy boy.

Seb Simpson (9)

Ottershaw Christ Church C of E Junior School, Bousley Rise
Ottershaw

Baby

The world is in pain!
Are you going to sit there?
Hurry up!
Save the planet!
Are you ashamed?
The fish are in pain
The flowers are dying!
Hurry!
Hurry!
The world is in pain
It's dreadful
You are monsters
You should be ashamed
You monsters
You are hurting Earth
Can you help?
Help
Hurry
Please help
Save
Earth

You are hurting the Earth
You monsters
You are evil
Feel ashamed
So stop
You monsters
Feel ashamed
Please help
I'm begging
You monsters
Feel ashamed
You have to help
Don't be sad
Just help
Please
Please
I'm begging
Help the Earth
Help us
Help everyone
Please

You are monsters
Why?
Help
Help
Help.

Riley Smith (9)

Ottershaw Christ Church C of E Junior School, Bousley Rise
Ottershaw

Endangered Animals

Do you really want to harm these cute animals?
They're endangered and scared out in the cold.
We need to try our best to save them and not put
plastic in the ocean.
Bad things will happen to the animals if you hurt
them.
Are you just going to sit on your sofa,
Or are you going to help us?
We are crying because there is too much plastic,
So help us by stopping putting plastic in the ocean.
Turtles are covered in plastic,
Turtle eggs are stuck in egg cartons,
So please help them.
They are battling plastic as much as they can,
But it is not enough, so help us.
We really, really, really, really need it.
Our shells are getting destroyed,
So help us, please.
I saw a baby turtle get destroyed by plastic, so
help,
And that's why you should save these animals.

Leia Fry (9)

Ottershaw Christ Church C of E Junior School, Bousley Rise
Ottershaw

Save Our Planet

Save our planet,
Don't treat it like a dump,
Rare, exotic animals are suffering,
Don't hurt these cute animals!
Who can deny that we're doing this?
We're about to let our favourite animals become
extinct!
Help them!

Save our planet,
Monkeys are choking on horrible, musty fumes.
They're homeless with nowhere to go.
Monkeys are dying.
Don't sit back and rest,
Help them!

Save our planet,
We're killing poor, innocent creatures.
Isolated polar bears drift away from their home
and family.
How would you feel if you were that polar bear?
Help them!

Please save them,
Don't let our planet die.
Animals will become extinct if you don't help now.
Save our planet!

Ella Keesing (9)

Ottershaw Christ Church C of E Junior School, Bousley Rise
Ottershaw

Help Poor Nature

We have all seen the ocean.

The emerald green turtles evacuating their family and homes.

No one wants to see the hopeless, innocent turtles getting extinct.

Help, the humans are throwing litter in the ocean, "Yum yum," the turtles die.

Would you like to leave your homes or say your final goodbyes?

The turtles are saying, "Help, my home is packed with loads of rubbish, I also can't move!"

The homeless polar bears floating on a tiny bit of ice, waving bye to their homes and families.

It's not safe for these innocent animals.

Swoosh! The air pollution storming in the sea.

Help, the animals are dying!

Come on England, why not help save our beautiful planet?

Leo Mans (8)

Ottershaw Christ Church C of E Junior School, Bousley Rise Ottershaw

Bad Environment

We've all seen the ocean with its luscious waves,
The sand is as soft as fluff,
But not anymore,
The ocean is like a dump,
All the rubbish thrown in the ocean is choking all
the animals,
Hurry and help,
Why not come save these poor, innocent animals
Rather than sitting on your comfortable sofa?
We've all seen birds,
Flying swiftly in the clean, fresh air,
But now, all that fresh air is gone,
The air is all musty,
We can't see any more birds because of us,
All the birds are choking,
The air pollution is taking over,
We need to stop this,
Hurry and help,
Stop playing on your video games and help these
animals!

Isabella Fraser-Edwards (8)

Ottershaw Christ Church C of E Junior School, Bousley Rise
Ottershaw

The Earth Is Falling Apart

The heartbroken polar bears,
Are losing their homes,
We need to help them,
What could you do to help?
May we save them,
The poor, innocent creatures are losing their homes,
Could you just let them pass or what?
Struggling to live,
We need to help them,
Their once-called home,
Come help, come help!
We need your love!
Monkeys' homes are catching on fire,
Come help, come help!
Please don't leave them,
And let them *live!*
Dying trees,
Get up please,
Get up with ease!

The trees,
Come help, come help!
They're going to yelp!

Chloe Custance (8)
Ottershaw Christ Church C of E Junior School, Bousley Rise
Ottershaw

Save Our Planet

Have you seen the rainforest?
Its trees all lush and green.
The animals are very exotic to look at.
How do you feel that the habitat is being destroyed by humans?
It was an amazing sight to see.
The glum, heartbroken family of monkeys stood next to a burning tree they once called home!
The choking, noxious smell made the birds unhealthy and faint.
Turtles are eating rubbish, dying as well.
The lonely polar bear stood on the cold, alone iceberg, shivering with no home.
All the broken pieces of rubbish were all surrounding the poor family of turtles.
Would you want to help these endangered animals?

Daisy King (8)

Ottershaw Christ Church C of E Junior School, Bousley Rise Ottershaw

Innocent But Endangered Animals

Are you sure you want to see precious animals drift away from their family?
We've all seen an ocean, a beautiful, blue ocean.
Animals are dying in that ocean, they're suffocating!
Why not help save those poor, cute animals with me?
How would you ever survive without trees?
Please don't chop down trees, they are saying, "I'm here to help people breathe, nothing that's bad, please don't get rid of me."
Animals are dying!
They are suffocating on plastic!
How would you feel if you were treated the same way?
Please help save them with me.
How could you help?

Gamila Rezk (9)

Ottershaw Christ Church C of E Junior School, Bousley Rise Ottershaw

Endangered Animals

Are you sure you want to see cute animals get drifted away from their amazing family?
We all like the sea, it is blue and magic.
But animals are being killed because you and many other people are throwing litter in the ocean. It has to stop!
Are you sure you are just going to let the poor animals drown in your rubbish?
Next stop, cutting down trees, the animals live there, so please stop cutting down trees.
Trees are a beautiful sight to see but you have to stop.
The poor animals are so sad.
It used to be beautiful and green until you humans destroyed the forest.
Please, please stop now!

Thomas Glover (9)

Ottershaw Christ Church C of E Junior School, Bousley Rise Ottershaw

Help The Planet

The Earth, the Earth is so amazing
So many things we do come from it
As well as the animals.
Why not help the planet from being destroyed?
Animals are losing their homes
So please try or you will say goodbye.
Are you just going to sit there
Or help me save the planet?
There is pollution in the air, plastic in the sea
Fires in the jungle, can't you see?
The polar bears are slowly floating away
From their homes and family.
Do you really want to see your favourite animals
extinct by humans?
Would you want to lose your home?
So come on, help me save the planet!

Iola Wilson (9)

Ottershaw Christ Church C of E Junior School, Bousley Rise
Ottershaw

The Extinction Is Starting Again

Why have you let this happen?
It's starting again.
The world is beautiful,
The planet is safe,
But now it's happening,
The extinction of pain.
Oh no, fix this,
The world is wrecked,
The world is in pain,
The world is suffocating,
The world is becoming lame once again.
Now, would you like to be treated this way?
Help us out, dude,
Don't just stand there.
The world's nature is hurt because of us,
Fix it with love or it's gonna get tough.
Help, help, help,
Don't let it get extinct,
So help our planet, please!

Abigail Bailey (9)

Ottershaw Christ Church C of E Junior School, Bousley Rise
Ottershaw

The Dreadful Forest

Are you going to help?
The animals are losing homes,
Can't you see that?
They are cold,
You need to do something about it,
Hurry, hurry,
Please help,
Do you want your favourite animals to be extinct?
How can you deny that humans are destroying the planet?
What can you do to help?

We have all seen the ocean,
Its waves are blue as the sky,
The waves are calmly bobbing the sea,
The animals are dying,
The fishermen throw nets in the animals' sea,
Do you want to let the animals suffocate from rubbish?
What can you do to help?

Mason Binnie (8)

Ottershaw Christ Church C of E Junior School, Bousley Rise
Ottershaw

Save Earth

S ave the planet, help the animals.

A nimals are losing their homes, can't you see that?

V ery little things can kill innocent animals.

E very little bit of plastic ruins the ocean.

E verything is going to die if you don't change things now!

A re you just going to sit there or are you going to help?

R eally, are you still cutting down forests?

T he abandoned, helpless animals sit devastated outside their glum, burning homes!

H ave you learned your lesson yet? Good!

Lilly Playford (8)

Ottershaw Christ Church C of E Junior School, Bousley Rise Ottershaw

Save The Planet

Animals are being extinct.
Trees are getting chopped down.
It breaks my heart.
How would you like it if you had to lose your home?
Animals are in danger.
Hurry, hurry!
Help the animals now!
The poor, innocent animals are losing their homes.
Help now!
Please help the animals that are suffering.
Would you like it if your favourite animal was gone forever?
Can you help the poor animals?
They really need your help!
Wouldn't you be heartbroken?
Help us have a healthy environment.
Save the planet.

Scarlett Ovenden (9)

Ottershaw Christ Church C of E Junior School, Bousley Rise Ottershaw

Help Save The Planet

Plastic is the murderer of fish, birds and wildlife,
We need to help our planet by buying less of it.
A turtle got stuck in a net,
He screamed for hours for help,
Nobody came.
He died a cruel and painful death.
Is this what you want?

A fox got his foot trapped in some plastic wire,
Caught for days with no food,
Suffering slowly, painfully,
Is this what you want?

A fish swallows, the birds are dying,
Well, how would you like it if it happened to you?
So stop and help the wildlife.

Oscar Alderman (8)

Ottershaw Christ Church C of E Junior School, Bousley Rise
Ottershaw

Save The World

Have you seen the rainforest?
If you have not, it's beautiful, amazing, a lovely sight to see.
But did you know the planet is in danger?
Come on!
Come on!
The starving, heartbroken turtle is suffocating in the sea of rubbish.
Do you want to help or do you want to see the planet die?
The horrified, cheerless polar bear floats alone on the shrinking ice it once called home.
Who doesn't want to help innocent, loving animals?
Stop taking them away from their homes.
Help save the world!

Lilly Tyler (8)

Ottershaw Christ Church C of E Junior School, Bousley Rise
Ottershaw

Animals

Animals are dying
Ice is melting
They are losing their homes
Let's get going
Save the planet
Mother Nature is not happy
Let's make the animals dance and the trees sing
Let's make plants smile
Let's go to nature
The polar bears are losing their homes on the ice
The ice is melting because of hot gas
Do you want to see your favourite animal extinct?
Let's go.

Arthur Williams (8)

Ottershaw Christ Church C of E Junior School, Bousley Rise
Ottershaw

Homes Of Animals Are Being Destroyed

Homes of animals are being destroyed,
Trees home to birds, beetles and bugs,
Will you just sit there or will you just help?
Polar bears float on an iceberg they once called
home,
Turtles eating junk,
Who can deny that we are guilty?
Homes of animals are being destroyed,
The poor birds choke on the noxious fumes,
Do you really know what we can do?
Now get up and help!

Owen Buckland-Waite (8)

Ottershaw Christ Church C of E Junior School, Bousley Rise
Ottershaw

How Can We Help?

Have a nice walk through a forest,
But you won't like what you hear,
Crash! Boom! The trees are falling to the ground.
Or go for a swim, but what?
It is filled with rubbish,
The poor animals are dying.
The car fumes are more dangerous than ever.
Come on England, how can we help?

Amelie Rippingham (9)

Ottershaw Christ Church C of E Junior School, Bousley Rise
Ottershaw

Why Earth Is Amazing

In the rainforest, people are chopping down trees
where animals are living
Would you like your home to be destroyed?
The populations of sea creatures are going down
Because of rubbish and pollution.
Did you know that trees are saving our lives?
Because trees give us air.

Annabelle Spall (8)

Ottershaw Christ Church C of E Junior School, Bousley Rise
Ottershaw

Help Save The Planet

We've all seen the ocean and it is bad
The sand is not soft, it is crumpled up.
In old, used plastic bottles
The crabs' homes are destroyed.
Come on England
Help save the planet.
Do you want to help?
Or do you want the planet to *die?*

Jack Dyson (8)

Ottershaw Christ Church C of E Junior School, Bousley Rise
Ottershaw

The Recycling Dragons

Help our planet: it doesn't cost any,
The people to be saved by:
Well, that's way more than many.

Wait a moment...
What was that?
Stealing rubbish from the cat?

Help our oceans: it doesn't cost any,
The people to be saved by:
Well, that's way more than many.

Wait a moment...
What's that I see?
Snatching rubbish from the sea.

"We're the dragon cleaning crew,
And we're here to help you!
To clean rubbish from this place,
And cure every single sad face."

Wilf Llewellyn
Pinewood School, Swindon

The Rainforest

The trees stretched and creaked
Their branches wispy and weak.
The insects scuttled and flew
While tigers pounced on grass, spraying dew.

Chameleons blended into the leaves
Whilst spiders built and weaved.
Sapphire blue rivers splashed and gushed
With water birds flying off in a rush.

Parrots screeched and squawked
Whilst leopards calmly walked.
Waterfalls twinkled and glittered
The forest floor covered and littered.

Please help before I get covered in plastic
This world of green is too fantastic.
We need to help and stop climate change
All this heat is really strange.

Now this is the end
So help us mend.
Let's stop pollution
And make a new revolution.

Tabitha Dean (9)
Pinewood School, Swindon

What Am I?

Tiny bugs and creepy spiders slowly crawl over me,
Tall trees tower over me,
Giant falling branches fall on me,
Wet rain barely gets to me,
Long sticks lie on me all day long,
Venturing humans trudge all over me,
The faint clouds float above me,
Beautiful birds fly smoothly around me,
Lush cut-down trees fall on top of me.
What am I?

Answer: The forest floor.

Bea Godfree (8)
Pinewood School, Swindon

Climate Change Is...

Climate change is bad for Earth
Climate change is global warming
Climate change is seas rising
Climate change is greenhouse gases overheating
Climate change is ice melting
Climate change is deforestation.

We can recycle more
We can turn off the lights
We can reduce fossil fuels
We can reduce our waste
We can eat less meat
We can stop global warming!

Freya Adderley
Pinewood School, Swindon

Recycle!

R educe and recycle

E veryone, don't throw plastic in the sea

C limate change is destroying our planet

Y ou should start recycling now!

C hange the world into a better place

L et the sea be free, don't get animals trapped in plastic

E veryone do your best and work together.

James Hosken (7)
Pinewood School, Swindon

Help Animals!

O ur planet is being destroyed
U p to us to clear up and
R ecycle rubbish.

P lastic bottles drowning the sea
L itter lying on the ground
A nimals thinking it is food
N ature is being destroyed
E veryone needs to help the planet
T ake your litter home!

Esme Walmsley (7)
Pinewood School, Swindon

Climate Change

A kennings poem

Planet destroyer
Ocean warmer
Ice melter
Greenhouse gas spewer
Plastic polluter
Wildlife waster
Rainforest ruiner
Earth eater
Wild radiator.

Wilfrid Bird (9)
Pinewood School, Swindon

The Rainforest

Deep in the noisy jungle,
Deep in the noisy jungle,
Colour feathers are on birds,
Deep in the colourful jungle,
There are slithering snakes like fish,
Deep in the loud jungle,
Is a fast waterfall,
Deep in the jungle,
Silly monkeys are jumping from tree to tree,
Deep in the annoying jungle,
Gorillas are boxing,
Deep in the quiet jungle,
Flamingos are dancing like ballerinas,
Deep in the busy jungle,
Scary tigers are swimming in a cold pond,
Deep in the hot jungle,
The sun is shining like Australia,
Deep in the freezing jungle,
The animals are very cold,
Deep in the cold jungle,
Some animals are eating their food.

Zawe Salahadin (7)
Rokeby Primary School, Rugby

The Jungle Of Nature

Deep in the peaceful jungle,
Water flows down the waterfall like a tap flowing,
Deep in the lousy jungle,
Birds are cheeping like a whistle,
Deep in the beautiful jungle,
Lovely trees are swaying gracefully in the breeze,
Deep in the helpless jungle,
Tigers are sneakily hunting their prey,
Deep in the loud jungle,
A gorilla is beating his chest like he's the boss,
Deep in the wild jungle,
Snakes are coiling around the tropical trees,
Deep in the colourful jungle,
Exotic flowers can be smelled,
Deep in the wonderful jungle,
Lush, green vines are tingling,
Deep in the hot jungle,
The sun is very hot like Egypt,
Deep in the gloomy jungle,
There is a cave that is forbidden,
Deep in the noisy jungle,

Pink flamingos are balancing like ballerinas,
Deep in the dark jungle,
The moon rises and everyone is asleep,
Deep in the sneaky jungle,
Someone is awake still.

Mariyah Ali (7)
Rokeby Primary School, Rugby

The Wild Jungle

Deep in the quiet jungle,
Birds sing their beautiful, elegant songs,
Deep in the silent jungle,
The tropical trees sway as the fruit slowly falls off
them and onto the ground,
Deep in the noisy jungle,
Tigers pounce at their helpless prey,
Deep in the loud jungle,
Colourful flowers bloom with brightness as bees
hop onto them and collect the nectar,
Deep in the beautiful jungle,
Butterflies fly over the swaying trees,
Deep in the lush jungle,
Moaning monkeys swing on tangled vines,
Deep in the dry jungle,
Tree frogs jump from tree to tree as fast as
lightning.

Rosie Harley (8)
Rokeby Primary School, Rugby

The Deep In The Jungle

Deep in the noisy, loud jungle,
The lake is rushing, tough water.
And colourful flamingos sing and dance.
And a rainbow parrot is squawking.
Hissing snakes,
Ferocious tigers,
Look for people to attack.
Roar roars the tiger,
And running so fast.
Animals are chatting.
The trees are swaying,
And the bush is swaying in the wind.
Wind comes,
Birds are singing elegantly,
Beautiful, colourful flowers,
Beautiful butterflies up in the sky.

Imani-Jane Mwananshiku Mnyanyika (7)

Rokeby Primary School, Rugby

The Glorious Forest

Deep in the disastrous jungle,
Golden tigers pounce on their prey and rip flesh
from their body,
Deep in the magical jungle,
Pink flamingos stand out in the gorgeous sunset
swinging their wings in the fresh air,
Deep in the colourful jungle,
Animals dancing with joy and love,
Deep in the mindful, calm jungle,
Animals resting and the sky turning black,
Now it is time to say goodbye to the sun
And all the fun things we did,
And now say hi to the moon.

Sameeha Ali (8)
Rokeby Primary School, Rugby

In The Dark Jungle

Deep in the magnificent jungle,
There was a stripy growling tiger and he was
sneakily looking for his prey,
In the dark jungle,
There was a noisy parrot that was copying
everything I said,
In the jungle,
There was an annoying toucan that was a hot,
coloured toucan,
In the dark scary jungle,
There were beautiful blooming flowers,
In the dark jungle,
There was a tree camouflaged frog that was
croaking and chilling on a green tree.

Nela Saja (8)
Rokeby Primary School, Rugby

The Sparkly Jungle Book

Deep in the calm water,
There are fish swimming and the tiger is trying to catch the fish,
Deep in the green forest,
It is green and beautiful, colourful and relaxing,
Deep in the green forest,
The tiger is sleeping and parrots are squawking,
Deep in the noisy jungle,
All of the animals are celebrating the tiger because the tiger is the boss,
Deep in the jungle,
Pink flamingos are dancing like a ballerina.

Veronica Barnes (8)

Rokeby Primary School, Rugby

Deep In The Jungle

The swaying trees and a branch.
The frog jumping high.
A tiger sings, oh roaring.
The parrot flies high.
The noisy toucans are on a branch.
The noisy toucans are scratching.
The colourful parrot flies high.
A frog splashes up high.
The colourful parrot flies.
The tiger is singing.
The frog splashes.

Millie Roche (7)
Rokeby Primary School, Rugby

Deep In The Jungle

Deep in the noisy jungle,
The parrots are soaring,
Deep in the quiet jungle,
A sneaky tiger is hungry,
Deep in the high jungle,
A snake is hiding in the trees,
Deep in the jungle,
A monkey is shouting at you.

Olly Stanhope (7)
Rokeby Primary School, Rugby

The Mouse

I am a tiny mouse.
I can touch the soft sticky mud.
I can see birds flying swiftly in the sky.
I can hear the raindrops dripping from the green leaves.
I can smell the fresh air early in the morning.

Izaiah Franklin (6)
Rokeby Primary School, Rugby

Deep In The Jungle

The angry tiger is roaring.
The colourful parrot sings on a branch.
The jumping frog splashes very tall.
A noisy toucan flies in water or the air.
The swaying trees are high.

Iumê Santiago (7)
Rokeby Primary School, Rugby

The Mouse

I am a mouse.
I can touch the soft, sticky mud.
I can see the tall rough trees stretching to the sky.
I can smell the damp leaves.
I can hear the tapping of the raindrops.

Kara Barnes (5)
Rokeby Primary School, Rugby

The Rabbit

I am a rabbit.
I can touch the squishy muddy floor.
I can smell the mushrooms on the floor.
I can see juicy apples in the trees.
I can hear the footsteps on the mud.

Daisy King (6)

Rokeby Primary School, Rugby

The Fox

I am a fox.
I can touch soft dirt.
I can see the leaves falling from the tree.
I can hear the whistling of the wind.
I can smell the air early in the morning.

Ethan Bingham (5)
Rokeby Primary School, Rugby

Deep In The Jungle

Deep in the noisy jungle,
Pink elegant flamingos are dancing like ballerinas,
Deep in the loud jungle,
There is a ferocious tiger,
The colourful parrot flies.

Meddina Marissa (8)

Rokeby Primary School, Rugby

The Fox

I am a fox.
I can touch crunchy leaves.
I can smell chickens hiding in the trees.
I can see mud on the ground.
I can hear music from the magical fairies.

Chevelle-Coco Marsden-Knole (6)
Rokeby Primary School, Rugby

The Fox

I am a fox.
I can touch the tree with spiky branches.
I can smell meat to eat.
I can see brown spiky trees.
I can hear birds singing.

Elliott King (5)
Rokeby Primary School, Rugby

Nature

Deep in the jungle, there is a pretty pink flamingo.
In the forest, there is a vicious tiger.
By the water, the butterfly flaps its wings.

Roxy Whisker (7)
Rokeby Primary School, Rugby

In The Jungle

A colourful elephant is singing.
The jumping frog splashes in the water.
A noisy tiger is roaring.
The colourful parrot is flying.

Luna Watts (7)
Rokeby Primary School, Rugby

The Rabbit

I am a rabbit.
I can touch the muddy floor.
I can smell stinky fish.
I can see a fox.
I can hear the birds eating seeds.

Matilda Rose Gravell (5)
Rokeby Primary School, Rugby

Deep In The Jungle

A noisy toucan flies to a branch.
The jumping frog chases in the water.
The tree is swaying high.
The angry tiger is roaring.

Matthew Barnes (8)
Rokeby Primary School, Rugby

The Rabbit

I am a rabbit.
I can touch mud.
I can smell burnt wood.
I can see spiky trees.
I can hear birds tweeting in the trees.

Lauren Ashby (6)
Rokeby Primary School, Rugby

Deep In The Jungle

Deep in the jungle,
Black gibbons are swinging and screaming.
Deep in the jungle,
Colourful birds are chirping happily.

Charlie Major (7)
Rokeby Primary School, Rugby

The Fox

I am a fox.
I can touch grass.
I can smell green leaves.
I can see red apples.
I can hear the trees shaking.

Harry Lusty Rule (5)
Rokeby Primary School, Rugby

The Fox

I am a fox
I can touch wild grass.
I can smell mud.
I can see fresh meat.
I can hear birds flapping.

Bailey Purchon (5)
Rokeby Primary School, Rugby

The Owl

I am an owl.
I can touch the long rough branches under my feet.
I can see the branch under the blue sky.

Brodie Spence (5)
Rokeby Primary School, Rugby

The Fox

I am a fox.
I can touch rock pools.
I can hear flowing water from a stream.
I can see tall trees.

Harvey White (6)
Rokeby Primary School, Rugby

In The Jungle

An angry tiger is roaring.
The frog splashes.
A branch falls off the tree.
A noisy toucan.

Edy Soare (8)
Rokeby Primary School, Rugby

The Bear

I am a bear.
I can touch spiky rocks.
I can smell mud.
I can see a cat.

Karolina Biczak (5)

Rokeby Primary School, Rugby

Help Earth

H ow can we help the environment?
E at healthy, don't waste any food.
L ove nature.
P rotect our plants and animals.

E very tree should be saved.
A nimals in the ocean need protecting.
R ecycle your rubbish.
T ake your bike or walk to school.
H elp the ocean by recycling plastic.

Nyah Pau (6)
Sandfield Close Primary School, Leicester

Nature

Nature has everything
Which is really amazing.
It has a blue sky
Where birds fly.
Drenching in rain
Gives us so much fun.
We feel the touch of wind
Which is cool and kind.
Let's make a promise to save Mother Earth.

Abheer Shetty (10)
Sandfield Close Primary School, Leicester

How To Save Earth

To save the Earth, do not chop trees.
To save the Earth, don't waste water and food.
To save the Earth, plant a tree.
To save the Earth, recycle things.
To save the Earth, be kind to Earth.

Kush Damani

Sandfield Close Primary School, Leicester

Thank You For The Rain

Thank you for the rain,
It sounds like waves crashing.
Thank you for the rain,
It looks like clouds crying.
Thank you for the rain,
It's really relaxing and clean.
Thank you for the rain,
It's as wet as a river.
Thank you for the rain,
It's life saving.
Thank you for the rain,
It's really refreshing.

Lacey-Mae Gandy (8)
Saviour CE Primary School, Collyhurst

Thank You For The Rain

Thank you for the rain,
It looks like stars shooting down.
Thank you for the rain,
It feels refreshing on my skin.
Thank you for the rain,
It's as clean as the wind.
Thank you for the rain,
It's as clear as glass.
Thank you for the rain,
It smells like wet leaves.

Ayomide Oyebade (8)
Saviour CE Primary School, Collyhurst

Thank You For The Rain

Thank you for the rain,
It looks like glitter falling from the sky.
Thank you for the rain,
It sounds like heavy footsteps.
Thank you for the rain,
It smells like wet leaves.
Thank you for the rain,
It feels like heavy drops on my skin.

Ivy
Saviour CE Primary School, Collyhurst

Thank You For The Rain

Thank you for the rain,
It looks like fish swimming.
Thank you for the rain,
It sounds like heavy hail stones.
Thank you for the rain,
It feels refreshing on my skin.
Thank you for the rain,
I feel wet raindrops dripping on my hand.

Lillie
Saviour CE Primary School, Collyhurst

Thank You For The Rain

Thank you for the rain,
It smells like fresh flowers.
Thank you for the rain,
It sounds like waves crashing.
Thank you for the rain,
It looks like shooting stars.
Thank you for the rain,
It sounds like a beating drum.

Teliah Kayembe (7)
Saviour CE Primary School, Collyhurst

Thank You For The Rain

Thank you for the rain,
It looks so lovely on the road.
Thank you for the rain,
It sounds like footsteps approaching.
Thank you for the rain,
It smells like wet leaves.
Thank you for the rain,
It is cold on my hands.

Josephine Awotide (8)
Saviour CE Primary School, Collyhurst

Thank You For The Rain

Thank you for the rain,
It sounds like waves crashing.
Thank you for the rain,
It smells like fresh air.
Thank you for the rain,
It looks like stars shooting.
Thank you for the rain,
It feels refreshing on my face.

Abel Peter Jinu
Saviour CE Primary School, Collyhurst

Thank You For The Rain

Thank you for the rain,
It smells very fresh.
Thank you for the rain,
It looks like falling stars.
Thank you for the rain,
It sounds like tapping on the roof.
Thank you for the rain,
It feels like wet leaves.

Brogan Bobmanuel (7)
Saviour CE Primary School, Collyhurst

Thank You For The Rain

Thank you for the rain,
It sounds like a storm brewing.
Thank you for the rain,
It is clear like glass.
Thank you for the rain,
It looks like stars shining.
Thank you for the rain,
It smells like wet leaves.

Azeemat

Saviour CE Primary School, Collyhurst

Thank You For The Rain

Thank you for the rain,
It looks like diamonds glowing.
Thank you for the rain,
It smells as fresh as detergent.
Thank you for the rain,
It is as damp as mud.
Thank you for the rain,
It is colder than snow.

Daisy Burgess (8)
Saviour CE Primary School, Collyhurst

Thank You For The Rain

Thank you for the rain,
It smells fresh and clean.
Thank you for the rain,
It looks like glitter in the sky.
Thank you for the rain,
It feels wet and damp.
Thank you for the rain,
It feels damp on my hands.

Eleri Vincent (7)
Saviour CE Primary School, Collyhurst

Thank You For The Rain

Thank you for the rain,
It sounds like a storm crashing.
Thank you for the rain,
It smells like fresh leaves.
Thank you for the rain,
It feels like fish.
Thank you for the rain,
It is as wet as a river.

Jaron
Saviour CE Primary School, Collyhurst

Thank You For The Rain

Thank you for the rain,
It smells like flowers.
Thank you for the rain,
It's clear like glass.
Thank you for the rain,
It sounds like the ocean crashing.
Thank you for the rain,
It is refreshing.

Tasia
Saviour CE Primary School, Collyhurst

Thank You For The Rain

Thank you for the rain,
It smells like wet leaves.
Thank you for the rain,
It is very calm.
Thank you for the rain,
It sounds like someone singing.
Thank you for the rain,
It looks like clear glass.

Jack Wilds (8)
Saviour CE Primary School, Collyhurst

Thank You For The Rain

Thank you for the rain,
It sounds like hail.
Thank you for the rain,
It is cold and wet.
Thank you for the rain,
It smells lovely.
Thank you for the rain,
It feels like water drops are on your hand.

Lyla
Saviour CE Primary School, Collyhurst

Thank You For The Rain

Thank you for the rain,
It sounds like footsteps.
Thank you for the rain,
It looks like diamonds.
Thank you for the rain,
It smells like wet leaves.
Thank you for the rain,
It makes me feel calm.

Tiara
Saviour CE Primary School, Collyhurst

Thank You For The Rain

Thank you for the rain,
It feels damp.
Thank you for the rain,
It looks like clear glass.
Thank you for the rain,
It smells like flowers.
Thank you for the rain,
It feels funny on my skin.

Owen
Saviour CE Primary School, Collyhurst

Thank You For The Rain

Thank you for the rain,
It looks damp.
Thank you for the rain,
It sounds like the wind is singing.
Thank you for the rain,
It smells like flowers.
Thank you for the rain,
It makes me cold.

Dia
Saviour CE Primary School, Collyhurst

Thank You For The Rain

Thank you for the rain,
It looks glittery.
Thank you for the rain,
It feels refreshing.
Thank you for the rain,
It smells fresh.
Thank you for the rain,
It feels calm.

Jacob
Saviour CE Primary School, Collyhurst

Thank You For The Rain

Thank you for the rain,
It smells like mint.
Thank you for the rain,
It feels like weeds.
Thank you for the rain,
It sounds like waves bashing.

Mustafa
Saviour CE Primary School, Collyhurst

Thank You For The Rain

Thank you for the rain,
It looks satisfying on the pavement.
Thank you for the rain,
It sounds relaxing.
Thank you for the rain,
It feels damp.

Ralphy
Saviour CE Primary School, Collyhurst

Friends Of Clear Water Fight For No Pollution

The water was as clear as crystal,
The ecosystem was beautiful.
The animals as calm as a lake.
But pollution is affecting everything:
The plants are crying out for help,
Animals all around you aching.
The animals are harmless and begging for support.
Rip! Splash! Humans are putting waste into the
ocean.
The rubbish in the current is dancing with
happiness.
Humans are so careless and animals are
desperate,
You could hear them cry a million times.
Creatures wishing they could live a bit longer,
Food webs destroyed,
Plastic gets ingested a lot.
It is not a fun world.
Why do people do this? I would really like to know.

Maryam Al-Saowaf (9)
St Leonards School, St Andrews

The Amazon Rainforest

Empty land of what used to be trees is now piles of not wanted leaves.
Animals' habitats being ruined, trees no longer living.
Big trees with beautiful leaves turning into our furniture needs.
The Amazon is screaming out for help but no one can hear its yelps.
Help the Amazon before it's too late, we should treat it as our best mate.

Animals running for their lives, while their friends die.
Stop all horrible humans hurting trees, it's too mean.
The animals are as scared as the trees.
The trees hear the terrifying roar of the chainsaw as it gets closer and closer, the tree is getting cut, It's falling until... *thump!* Yet another tree gone.

Every animal tries to hide, but they know they'll be found.
The Amazon soon to give up, all these years of trying have done no good.

Less and less by the second, less trees, less animals, the planet is dying, slowly dying, very, very slowly, but soon to get faster.

In the end, there will be no world, or humans at all, all life will be dead.

Michelle Chernin (9)
St Leonards School, St Andrews

Coral

Coral, beautiful coral,
Drying up with global warming,
Coral colour draining with the sea's cold, slowly
but surely,
Coral, full of life,
Bathed in its hopefully never-ending bath: the
great sea,
Oh, coral, what would we do without you?
Almost no point in coral diving,
Go to the sea, see the waves, but you won't see the
beauty beneath,
Coral curled, clumped coral,
Right are people who do beach clean-ups,
Wrong are people who throw plastic in the ocean,
Crash! Boom! go the sad waves as they wash up
plastic,
Coral, many different colours, shapes and sizes,
Absolutely beautiful home of many different fish,
Or hiding place to hide from sharks, octopuses and
bigger fish,
Long has coral been on this planet,

Coral has been here for longer than us humans,
Coral should be here forever more.

Jos Norris-Mbedzi (10)

St Leonards School, St Andrews

The Crocodile

The water shimmers brightly
And the crocodile lurks secretly
Through the water to ambush a zebra
That is crossing the shiny, shimmering water.

The crocodile jumps on its back and kills it
After a fight the zebra thinks to itself, *oh*
Maybe I should have gone to the zebra crossing.

He cries out big heavy tears
The crocodile smiles and smirks
At the other zebras, it lurks
Secretly through the muddy
Water to the zebra crossing.

And the rocks cry in the water
Because of plastic bottles of petrol coming down
the river.

George Cheape (9)
St Leonards School, St Andrews

The Underwater Urgency

The water freezing on my body.
The kelp slimy.
The sea urchins spiking my hand,
And nibbling my fingers, it tickles.
Fish skimming my tummy,
And talking to me and taking me to their house,
And giving me my tea.
Now there are no more fish in the sea.
I feel guilty, so we must stop!
Now the sharks are chasing us.
The sea washing water in my mouth, it tasting
salty.
We have to restore the fish!
Stop fishing to let the fish flee from our frantic
frenzy.
If we don't, the fish will go extinct!

Dylan Pyne-Carter (9)

St Leonards School, St Andrews

The Tundra

Tundra, tundra,
The snow sparkling as the sun rises early in the morning,
Tundra, tundra,
Mountains are towering over the mighty trees,
Tundra, tundra,
The snow is as white as paper,
Tundra, tundra,
Where the mighty moose roams,
Tundra, tundra,
The scenery is as beautiful as me,
And the wind is so strong that
The leaves are dancing on the trees,
Tundra, tundra,
Crash! Boom!
An avalanche, the moose run for their lives,
Climate change,
Tundra, tundra.

Martha Kavanagh (9)
St Leonards School, St Andrews

Reefs At Risk!

The coral reef, so calm and shiny,
So warm and cold,
So kind and bold.
But the sea is crying its deep, salty tears,
As the plastic chokes it violently.
And the waves are screaming with all their might
as their rage slowly rises,
The plastic is dragging the animals to the bottom
of the ocean.
Scaly fish too scared to swim and oily squid too
scared to squirt their ink,
This ecosystem's on the brink.
Slash! Bang! goes the sea.
"Help, argh!" scream fishies.

Elin Tausch (9)
St Leonards School, St Andrews

Kelp Forest

In the dark and murky water where the sea is
silently moving.
There's a problem.
I feel unwell, things are swirling in me.
I am getting warmer every day.
I see nets and bottles.
I see rods as long as a giraffe.
I see fish scared like they have seen a monster.
It's me, the sea, why can't you see?
I taste plastic in my mouth.
It makes me so sad.
It drives me mad!
Help me!
I say help!

Stop this ticking time bomb called Earth!

Claudia Breen (9)
St Leonards School, St Andrews

Extinction

Crash! Bang! went the trees bashing on the
ground,
Buzz! Hum! went the bees watching their home
disappear,
All the orangutans become extinct,
The shampoo supply is as massive as an elephant,
The stunning sun sneakily rises
People stumble in,
They wander out,
And the smell is worse than a bin!
The plastic is waving at you in the wind,
Help our planet and save us and animals from
going extinct.

Isabella Hawkins (9)
St Leonards School, St Andrews

Deforestation

Drip, drop, the warm rain is pounding on the
ground
And the river is as mucky as a pigsty
Oh no, not now, the trees are getting cut down
Will I be next?
I can hear the chainsaw coming closer
I can taste the dust
And smell the sap
I can hear screams
They are not so distant
Is that *Samantha?*
My friend!
Those stunning sapphire flowers were Samantha's
favourites.

Thea Steven (10)
St Leonards School, St Andrews

Wetlands

The water is rising up to the trees
Fish swimming around the tall tree
The big, thick tree had animals inside it
Fish eat the grass on the tree
The water is chilly
Frosty water moving calmly
Animals moving slowly
I can see animals in the water splashing around
I can hear the wind moving the tree forwards and
backwards
I can hear snakes hissing from far away.

Abdulla Al Ajami (9)
St Leonards School, St Andrews

The Great Barrier Reef

I can taste the sea's bitter tears.
It is as stormy as a thunderstorm.
The waves are running away from the plastic as
fast as they can.
The animals are almost extinct.
The Earth is dying and the sea is crying.
Pollution is going to win.
Help the sea, help me and then we can win.

Priya Myles (9)
St Leonards School, St Andrews

Deforestation

The bright green grass is waving gently with the
wind.
The lion is as sneaky as a black panther.
I can hear the tree whooshing gently with the
grass
And the lion's roar is so loud it hurts my ears.
Stop deforestation!
The tree stands still as the lion sleeps.

Amber McGhee (9)
St Leonards School, St Andrews

Animal Extinction

It was a bright, sunny day,
I went to the zoo with Winnie the Pooh,
As we strolled along peacefully, we saw:

A beautiful black panther roaming its grounds,
Two giant anteaters, their heads in a mound,
A crazed-looking hyena laughing away,
And four tiny chipmunks enjoying the day.

Greeting me were roughly ten friendly fish,
We saw seven sharks chomping on a dish,
Pingu and his friends sped down the slides,
And Eve the elephant took five humongous strides.

Silly Sammy the snail slipped under a rock,
Whilst the children grew impatient, *knock, knock, knock!*
Alex the armadillo armed for war,
As Tommy the tiger stretched his prodigious paw.

Suddenly, Gerry the giraffe popped his neck out,
This startled the children without a doubt,

Quickly, five immense tigers ran after their prey,
Then the kind, caring bears said, "They'll need an x-ray!"

All these beautiful animals, so splendid and free,
Will be close to extinction unless we act quickly,
So I call upon you all to stop and listen,
Stop destroying rainforests and causing pollution,
Let's all gather together and be part of the solution.

Ibrahim Mukhtar (8)

St Martin's Preparatory School, Grimsby

My World, My Home, My Earth

O ur planet, Earth, the one and only, the most beautiful.

U nexplored areas yet to be discovered.

R ainforests are Earth's oldest living ecosystem.

P lants occupy eighty percent of Earth.

L iving creatures as small as bacteria and as big as a mammoth have lived here for centuries.

A nimals that live here make our life wonderful.

N itrogen, oxygen and carbon dioxide are a few of the gases found over here.

E lements like gold, silver and copper are mined from the deepest parts of Earth.

T errestrial ecosystems comprised of biotic and abiotic components.

And that's my world,
That's my home,
That's my Earth.

Zayn Zafar (9)
St Martin's Preparatory School, Grimsby

Spring In My Garden

Nature's waking from a long, deep sleep,
The sun is shining down the creek.
Daffodils in bright sunshine yellow,
Hyacinths in pastel pink,
Tulips swaying in the wind.
Ladybirds rest on nettle leaves,
Tiny red dots in seas of green.
Birds are chirping, building nests,
Their hungry chicks won't let them rest.
Bees are busy working hard,
Gentle humming fills the air,
Nature's wonders everywhere.
Build a hedgehog house or a bug hotel.
These little things will truly help,
Time to show how much you care!

Noel Gacs (8)
St Martin's Preparatory School, Grimsby

They Once Were, We Can Change

If we don't take care of them
They will all become extinct
And we will be one of them
We are not very distinct.

A dodo was a metre tall
And its feathers didn't fall
With a diet full of fruit
Humans just gave them the boot.

Woolly mammoths disappeared
Easily hunted with a spear
They were four metres tall
And had a special call.

With dark stripes, two metres long
It's the Tasmanian tiger, strong
Killed in 1921 and extinct in '36
We are missing the tiger's tricks.

Baji dolphin, dinos too
Sabertooth cat, passenger pigeon
They were all one in a million
Let all animals be free, just like me and you.

Aideen Brusby (8)

St Martin's Preparatory School, Grimsby

The Environment

Roses are red, violets are blue,
I love plants and you do too.
Save our trees, they're going down, we're harming
our environment,
To lose them would be such a disappointment.
All our colours will be gone,
If our plants and trees aren't strong.
All our insects big and small and beautiful,
Even bees and all will be lost as well
Help me save our world very quickly,
So it will be a better environment.

Tatenda Mutondo (8)
St Martin's Preparatory School, Grimsby

My Life By Mr Fox

W ild and free is how I like to be.

I feel good and calm in the wild.

L et the leaves fall so I can play.

D ancing with my friends to the sound of the wind.

L ying in the sunshine after a dip in the river.

I like running free in the wild.

F un and laughter with my friends.

E ating a picnic when watching the sunset.

Henry Evans (8)

St Martin's Preparatory School, Grimsby

The Boy Who Lay In The Barn

The boy lay with the dog who wasn't a stray
And the paint was grey on the rickety barn.
The boy and the dog rolled in the hay
To keep warm because outside was cold
In the barn that was old
On the boy's grandpa's farm.
Then from the cottage shouted Mum,
So the boy jumped off his bum,
And the dog ran along too,
As it was their favourite stew.

Felix Bristow (9)
St Martin's Preparatory School, Grimsby

Environment

E verybody needs to help
N ever throw rubbish out the window
V ery happy animals
I help clean
R ubbish is bad for the world
O ur planet is incredible
N ot in the ocean
M any animals are scared
E verybody
N eeds to put rubbish in the bin
T ogether we can help the world.

Amelia Philips (6)

Townhill Community School, Townhill

Environment

E nvironment
N ot throwing rubbish
V ery wet and rainy
I hope the world gets better
R ecommend that people recycle
O n my journey
N ests in the trees
M y family is loving
E at some chicken
N asty smell of pollution
T idy our planet.

Rossi-Leigh Davies (7)

Townhill Community School, Townhill

Environment

E nvironment.

N aughty people throwing rubbish.

V ery wet and soggy.

I am born in the forest.

R ecycle.

O range leaves.

N ests high in the sky.

M ake a difference.

E arth is the best planet.

N ight is peaceful.

T he world is strong.

Shae Griffin (7)

Townhill Community School, Townhill

Habitat

H ome is where I live, it is a big house.
A rctic is where the black and white penguins live.
B rown bears live in the dark forest.
I nsects live in dirty, brown mud.
T he smelly animals live on a farm.
A turtle lives in the blue sea.
T he blue whale lives in the cold ocean.

Olivia Williams (7)

Townhill Community School, Townhill

Environment

E nvironment.

N o throwing paper at animals.

V ery wet and soggy.

I was looking for animals.

R ecycling.

O range leaves.

N o signal in the forest.

M um, can you please help?

E lephants are good.

N ature.

T he world is strong.

Kieran Lott (7)

Townhill Community School, Townhill

Habitat

H ome is where I live.

A rctic is cold, where black and white penguins live.

B ears live in dark, black caves.

I nsects live in the green leaves.

T he pigs live on a muddy farm.

A whale lives in the blue sea.

T igers live in the hot, sticky jungle.

Isla-Rae Pryor (7)

Townhill Community School, Townhill

Environment

E nvironment
N ight-time
V ery hot
I am happy in the forest
R eally soggy in the forest
O n the flowers there are bugs
N ever hurt animals in the forest
M essy in the forest
E nemy
N ature
T arget.

Stefan Hascec (6)
Townhill Community School, Townhill

Environment

E nvironment.
N o to pollution.
V ery hot forest.
I 'm very wet.
R ecycle.
O range trees.
N ot people.
M essy forest.
E very animal is pretty.
N ests in the forest.
T igers are pretty.

Kiki Morris (7)

Townhill Community School, Townhill

Habitat

H elp the animals, they need food
A nimals need help with looking where they are going
B e kind to the animals
I am flabbergasted
T ake care of our planet
A nimals need to be happy
T rees need help.

Elodi-Mai Norman (7)
Townhill Community School, Townhill

Habitat

H elp the sad animals.
A nimals need looking after.
B e kind to the sad planet.
I need to make the planet better.
T eamwork is key.
A nimals need big help.
T rust the planet.

Isabelle O'Connor (6)

Townhill Community School, Townhill

Habitat

H elp the animals.
A m cross with people.
B ecause they are in danger.
I love all animals.
T all and small.
A nimals deserve love.
T ogether we will help.

Lottie Smith (7)

Townhill Community School, Townhill

Habitat

H elp the sad planet

A m dumbfounded

B e kind to animals

I am flabbergasted

T rees give us air

A nd I am sad

T hat we are killing our planet.

Deacan Griffiths (7)

Townhill Community School, Townhill

Habitat

H elp the animals
A id the planet
B e kind to the Earth
I like the Earth
T hough I
A m flabbergasted
T ell the world.

Koby Johansen (6)

Townhill Community School, Townhill

Earth

E xcellent place to live.
A nimals live on Earth.
R ocks are underground.
T he Earth is beautiful.
H appy world.

Eviee-Mae Smith-Ham (6)
Townhill Community School, Townhill

The Clear White Season

On the ice at night,
A deep crack rumbles underground.
The moon shines so brightly,
Then winter is so clear white.
The abominable yeti,
Lurking around the snow.
Everything is cold,
Just like the ice-cold blizzard.
Coldness lurks in the tundra,
The Arctic is cold.
The polar bears go seeking,
Then penguins have fun.
It is a clear white season,
Mountains stand so tall,
After all, it is so grand.
White snow is joyous,
And it is such good fun,
Then when you play in the snow,
Snow makes you cold.

Abdur Rehman Chaudhry (11)
Varna Community Primary School, Openshaw

Seasons

Haiku poetry

Spring
Crunchy grass crunching
The world full of happiness
Flowers blossoming.

Summer
Sun heating the world
Ice cream melting in your mouth
Beaming sun burning.

Autumn
Leaves falling from trees
Flowers blowing in the breeze
Swaying grass blowing.

Winter
Wintertime is here
Snowflakes falling all around
Freezing up rivers.

Scarlett Tarrant (11)

Varna Community Primary School, Openshaw

Global Warming

H eaps of deadly fumes
E xpelled by careless cars
A waste of precious materials
T hat could have been recycled
I f we stay green
N ot continuously doing our dirty ways
G reen Earth might decide to stay.

Kolade Oyewo (11)
Varna Community Primary School, Openshaw

Snow

S ilence, it's winter.

N ow is your time to save our animals

O nly up to you now

W ill you save our future?

Indy Davies (11)

Varna Community Primary School, Openshaw

YOUNG WRITERS INFORMATION

We hope you have enjoyed reading this book – and that you will continue to in the coming years.

If you're the parent or family member of an enthusiastic poet or story writer, do visit our website **www.youngwriters.co.uk/subscribe** and sign up to receive news, competitions, writing challenges and tips, activities and much, much more! There's lots to keep budding writers motivated!

If you would like to order further copies of this book, or any of our other titles, then please give us a call or order via your online account.

Young Writers
Remus House
Coltsfoot Drive
Peterborough
PE2 9BF
(01733) 890066
info@youngwriters.co.uk

Join in the conversation!
Tips, news, giveaways and much more!

f YoungWritersUK   **𝕐** YoungWritersCW   **⊙** youngwriterscw

Scan me to watch The Big Green video!